How to Write
LETTERS *for* HEALING

A WORKBOOK

How to Write
LETTERS *for* HEALING

*A Guide to Using the Therapeutic Power of Writing
to Overcome Grief*

VON KOPFMAN C.M.P
AUTHOR OF THE *Letters For Healing* SERIES OF BOOKS

How to Write Letters For Healing
A Guide to Using the Therapeutic Power of Writing to Overcome Grief

By Von Kopfman C.M.P.

© Copyright Von Kopfman 2022

MISSION POINT PRESS
2554 Chandler Road
Traverse City, MI 49696
www.MissionPointPress.com
231.421.9513

Printed in the United States of America

ISBN: XXXXX
Library of Congress number 2013933682

Visit the author at www.thelastsongwriter.com/emotional

To listen to songs Von created to accompany his *Letters for Healing* series, scan the QR code below:

Please note: Von is accepting submissions for future editions of *Letters for Healing.* Please email your letter and contact information to forthesurvivors@hotmail.com.

"To write is human, to receive a letter: Divine."

— SUSAN LENDROTH

How to Write
LETTERS for HEALING

Introduction

THIS LETTER-WRITING GUIDE is designed to work in concert with the Letters for Healing series of books and will help guide you toward hand-writing your own letters to deal with your grief or loss experience. Whether the grief is caused by the actual physical loss of a loved one or the end of a career, marriage, or friendship, the grieving process is very much the same. It seems that in this post-pandemic world, even the loss of community and a sense of isolation can elicit similar grief responses. So, it is logical that the same tools of putting pen to paper can open those channels of communication that seemed closed.

Writing a letter has become a lost art, and the biggest challenge is where to start?

That is the purpose of this letter-writing guide – to help you begin the process of writing your letters and find the healing process provided by narrative therapy.

Remember … just because you write the letter does not mean you have to share it. The healing is in the writing, the power is in the work. There is no shame in openly expressing the wide range of emotions you are feeling, and no need to fear what someone else might think of it. These feelings are your own, and no one can tell you what you are feeling is wrong. Own them, write them down, be specific, let it all out, take your time, feel the relief.

It is my sincere hope that this letter-writing guide will help you begin the process of healing and begin a lifetime of dealing with your struggles in a healthy way.

Von Kopfman

"I write to give myself strength,
I write to be the characters I am not, I write to explore
all the things I am afraid of."
— Joss Whedon

How to Use This Letter-Writing Guide:
Frequently Asked Questions

I see that this workbook includes a lot of "prompts" – suggested words to start my letter. Do I have to use the prompts, and what is their purpose?

In an age of technology, emails, social media, spell check, etc., handwriting a letter has largely gone out of fashion. The purpose of the prompts is to simply help you get started with your handwritten letter and your journey toward healing. You certainly do not have to use them; they are merely there to help you begin that conversation. You can definitely create your own.

How much should I write?

Write as little or as much as you feel comfortable. This is not a quantity but rather a quality exercise. The work, the therapeutic value, is in the writing and the associated release of emotions. There is no right or wrong. It has been reported that people are often surprised by how much they have written when they have finished a particular writing session.

Should I outline my thoughts first?

Organizing your thoughts prior to writing diminishes the emotional release associated with handwriting the letter. It is proven to be of more therapeutic value to just write and let it flow, much like an actual conversation.

Should I have a friend or family member read what I write once I'm done?

This is completely up to you. Some feel best sealing and filing away the letter immediately upon completion; some will carry the letter and re-read it over and over, even adding to the letter as time passes. In sharing your letter, do what feels natural to you so long as the potential for sharing does not diminish your honesty in the letter. Remember ... these are your thoughts and feelings and yours alone. No one has the right to judge or critique how you feel about a loss or traumatic situation.

What should I be thinking about internally when I write?

Think of it in terms of a conversation. Share with the lost loved one everything you are thinking and feeling. Do not hold back, do not worry about spelling or grammar, think about everything you want to communicate and do so honestly.

How does this help me? What happens inside me to make this writing worth it to me?

Handwriting letters to deal with trauma is part of what's called "narrative therapy." Narrative therapy has been used for years to express feelings that are either impossible to share − due to, say, death of a loved one − or too difficult because of a fear of an unfavorable reaction. When you handwrite a letter or letters to deal with trauma or loss, you release real emotions ... much the same as if you had an actual conversation, and often even more because there is no rebuttal. What you feel is release, a transfer of energy. You feel better. When you have finished the letter, you may want to hold a personal ceremony and shred or burn what you wrote. Destroying the letter can help complete the process. But that's not required. Some folks prefer to hold on to their letters. Do what feels natural to you.

Will writing these letters get easier with time?

The short answer is yes. Like anything worth doing, self-care requires discipline. The practice of putting pen or pencil to paper will get easier as you get into the rhythm and habit of doing so. As you write more and feel the release and see the value, you will likely find more to write about: repressed traumas from years past, current events that have you angry or upset – the possibilities are almost endless. As you develop the habit of using this tool, you will likely use it more.

Some of your prompts deal more with anger; others with brokenness. How do I choose?

With any traumatic event, there are a myriad of emotions that will be released: anger, depression, sadness, desperation, disbelief, regret. Some will arrive all at the same time, some not until years later. While a few of the prompts may seem irrelevant now, they may become very relevant as you begin to write and get in touch with all of the emotions you are feeling. The prompts are merely there to help you get started, but do not let them limit you in what you choose to write. Remember … whatever you are feeling is OK and even natural. Write them down and let them go.

It is my hope that this guide will help you move in a more positive direction toward healing. Remember that your journey is yours and yours alone; there is no right or wrong, and no timeline for completion. The important part is getting started, and the best time is now.

This book is no substitute for therapy if you feel it is needed. Please seek a competent professional that specializes in grief and can provide references.

Best of luck on your journey toward healing. Now write that letter!

Your LETTERS *for* HEALING
... with suggested words for starting them.

Today I woke up and remembered _____

I feel very alone today and _____

I am very angry and _____

Life seems so unfair.

Do you know how much I _____

_____ *asked about you yesterday,*

The kids are _____

"Letter-writing is the only device for combining solitude with good company."

— LORD BYRON

I hate this situation.

Could you just help me understand?

I guess what I miss most is ...

I want to start with I am sorry.

Where do I begin?

I'm sitting here in the dark thinking …

Every day I think about ...

"Letter-writing is an excellent way
of slowing down this lunatic,
helter-skelter universe long enough
to gather one's thoughts."
– NICK BANTOCK

I just want one more _____

I wish we had the chance to ...

Well, it's almost your birthday.

I will never forget that time we _____

I hurt, my head, my heart _____

I do not want to write this, but …

"I realize how valuable the art and practice of writing letters are, and how important it is to remind people of what a treasure letters — hand-written letters — can be."

— Nancy Reagan

How could you _____*?*

It is hard to know what to say.

I think of you so often.

It has been_____ years, how?

Although I never told you,

If only I had known about _____

Since I was small, I believed _____

"Writing letters is good for you."

— BILL BAILEY

You are always with me.

I still don't know how to answer _____

Good morning.

So much has changed since _____

You will forever be _____

I miss the conversations.

"Writing isn't letters on paper.
Its communication, its memory."

— ISAAC MARION

Time keeps moving but I cannot.

Living without you is _____

It is so hard to believe it has been _____

I still feel you here.

Your things are where you left them.

Too High a Price to Pay
Song and lyrics by Von Kopfman

No one knows the hell I'm going through, since you have gone away
Each day I put a smile on like some well-worn shirt,
so no one sees my pain
But inside a part of me has died and I'm dying more and more each day
When I'm alone tears for you fill my eyes losing you
was too high a price to pay

People say how I seem so strong they can't believe that I'm so well
What they can't know is I'm not the same I bury the brokenness
so they can't tell
That inside my heart wants to explode nothing seems to take the hurt away
When I'm alone the emotions uncontrolled losing you
was too high a price to pay

Only God has the answers why things turned out this way

Still, I wake up every morning I greet you hoping that you hear
Going through the motions counting down the days death
no longer holds any fear
But inside I just want to scream it's never going to be ok when I'm alone
I come apart at the seams
Losing you was too high a price to pay, losing you
was too high a price to pay

To hear other songs in the *Letters for Healing* series,
scan this QR code.

To submit your letter for consideration in future editions
of *Letters for Healing*, send letter and full contact information to:
von_music@hotmail.com

Made in the USA
Columbia, SC
30 August 2022

66016407R10057